Dad's Bathtime

Our dad likes to take a bath.
He thinks in the tub.
He sings in the tub.
He even reads in the tub.

3

Yesterday we caught some frogs. We brought them home, but they wouldn't stay in the bucket.

4

So we put the frogs in the tub.

Then Dad came home.
"I think I'll take a bath," he said.

8

"What about a shower?" we said.

"You can't read in the shower," said Dad.

"There's a great game on TV,"
we said.

"You can't read *and* watch TV," said Dad. "I just want to take a bath."

13

15

Our dad likes to take a bath —
even with frogs!

16